I Love My Mami!

by Judy Katschke   illustrated by Dave Aikins

SCHOLASTIC INC.

New York Toronto London Auckland Sydney
Mexico City New Delhi Hong Kong Buenos Aires

Hi! I am Dora!

I am going to spend
the day with my **mami**.

First we feed the babies.

Then we make a
yummy breakfast.

My **mami** takes me with her to work.

Look what I found!

Then **Mami** and I
go to the park.

We play on the swings.
Higher and higher we go!

I made a present
for **Mami.**

It is a picture of us!

Mami and I
had a great day.

I love my **mami**!
And **Mami** loves me.